The Adventures of
MANUEL
& DIDI

ERWIN MOSER

The Adventures of
MANUEL & DIDI

Winter Stories

Translated by Philip Nokes

Scholastic Children's Books,
Scholastic Publications Ltd,
7-9 Pratt Street, London NW1 OAE

Scholastic Inc.,
730 Broadway, New York, NY 10003, USA

Scholastic Canada Ltd,
123 Newkirk Road, Richmond Hill,
Ontario L4C 3G5, Canada

Ashton Scholastic Pty Ltd,
P O Box 579, Gosford, New South Wales,
Australia

Ashton Scholastic Ltd,
Private Bag 1, Penrose, Auckland,
New Zealand.

First published by Beltz Verlag, Weinham und Basel 1987 under the titles
Manuel & Didi Die Baümhutte and *Manuel & Didi Der Schneemensch*

This edition published by Scholastic Publications Ltd, 1993

ISBN 0 590 54131 5

10 9 8 7 6 5 4 3 2 1

Contents

AUTUMN STORIES

1. The Tube   *Page* 9
2. The River Ghost   *Page* 16
3. The Bunch of Grapes   *Page* 23
4. The Owl   *Page* 30
5. The Leaf House   *Page* 37
6. The Tree House   *Page* 44

WINTER STORIES

1. The Ice Boat   *Page* 53
2. The Bridge   *Page* 60
3. The Snowman   *Page* 67
4. The Badger's House   *Page* 74
5. The Pumpkin Sledge   *Page* 81
6. The Cheese   *Page* 88

AUTUMN STORIES

The Tube

"Manuel, I've found a rather strange
Thing," says Didi to his friend one day.
He takes Manuel along to a hollow in
the ground and points down.

The Thing is a tube of paint. The two
mice touch it and sniff it.
"Can you feel something moving
inside?" asks Manuel.

They climb up on to the tube and jump
around. It's great fun. The tube is
squidgy and changes its shape
underneath them.

"I think you can open the Thing if you turn this yellow cap," says Manuel.

He unscrews the cap. Suddenly a long
pink sausage shoots out at top speed.

"Heeelp!" scream Manuel and Didi. "A snake! Help!" But this snake isn't going to bite anyone, is it?

The
River Ghost

One evening Didi decides to visit
Norbert the water rat who lives on an
island in the middle of the river. But
what's that? He sees something terrible
on the island and is afraid to go.

The next day Didi tells Manuel what
happened.
"A terrible monster lives on Norbert's
island," he says. "He has a green head
and yellow eyes."

In the evening Didi and Manuel creep
down to the edge of the river.
"Oh," whispers Manuel. "That's
definitely a river ghost. He must have
locked Norbert up in the house. We've
got to help him, Didi."

They pluck up their courage and row
across to the island. "I'll say something
to the ghost," says Manuel."Perhaps that
will make him disappear."

"Great river ghost, we are not afraid of you," says Manuel. "Please let Norbert go. He is our friend and the dearest water rat on the whole river. Please, go away."

Suddenly, Norbert steps out from the
bushes. He is a bit embarrassed.
"It's very kind of you to rescue me," he
says. "But I made this pumpkin ghost
myself, and he won't harm anyone."

The
Bunch of
Grapes

One day on his walk Manuel comes
across a vine. A large juicy bunch of
grapes looks down at him from
between the leaves.

Then Didi turns up as well.
"Look up there, Didi," says Manuel.
"That could be our lunch. Lift me up
and I'll pick some of the grapes."

Manuel climbs on to Didi's head and
reaches up.
"Don't wobble, Didi." But what a pity –
the grapes are too high.

Then Manuel has an idea.
"Wait here, Didi. I'll be back in a
minute." He runs off home and comes
back with his catapult.

Manuel fires at the grapes with his
catapult. Splosh! He hits them, and the
tasty juice drops into Didi's mouth.

He fires again at the grapes and more
juice trickles down. The two mice drink
to their hearts' content.

The Owl

"Look!" says Manuel to Didi. "Those bushes over there are like flying monsters."

Didi shows Manuel a dead tree.
"Don't you think it looks just like an old
giant?"
Manuel agrees.

"And look at this haystack, Didi. It's a mammoth."

Then they come across a dying
sunflower.
"It could be an old lady who has been
put under a spell," says Didi.

In the evening they discover a group
of rocks.
"This rock looks like an owl," says
Manuel.

The 'rock' opens its eyes and spreads its
wings.

"You need to wear glasses," he says. "I
am an owl!"

The
Leaf House

In the last few weeks the leaves have
turned brown and yellow and fallen off
the trees. Manuel and Didi are playing
among them.

"Do you know what?" says Manuel. "We can build ourselves a leaf house." "Great!" cries Didi. They make a frame out of some thin sticks.

Then they put hundreds of leaves on it.
It's hard work, but at last they finish it.
It looks almost like a Red Indian tent.

Manuel and Didi creep into their little
house and lie down on the rustling
leaves.
"Now tell me a funny story, Didi," says
Manuel.

Whoosh! Suddenly a great gust of wind comes and blows away all the leaves.

Only the crooked frame is left. Manuel
and Didi are amazed.
"That wasn't very funny, Didi," says
Manuel.

The
Tree House

The days and nights have become very
cold. So Manuel and Didi are looking
for a warm home. They like the look of
a hollow tree.

They fetch some straw and branches to
build a roof over the tree stump.
"This will be the best house we've ever
had," says Didi.

The two mice settle down in their new
house. But it isn't very warm.
"We need a good stove," says Manuel.

They set off to look for a stove, and
meet a rabbit. Manuel has an idea.
"Come along with us," he says to the
rabbit.

"Look, there's our house. Do you want to see inside?"
The rabbit wants to have a look and so goes with them.

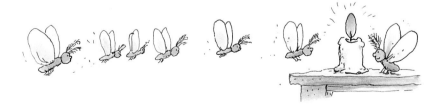

The rabbit likes the house and decides
to stay for the night. Manuel and Didi
rest against his warm fur – so much
better than a stove!

WINTER
STORIES

The Ice Boat

The lake has frozen over. Manuel and
Didi have built themselves an ice boat,
and the wind drives it along.

They see some holes in the ice, and a
fish pops out of one of them.
"Help me," he cries. "The bear wants to
catch me."

Manuel has an idea to make the bear go
away. He gets some black paint and
draws a horrible face on the sail of the
boat.

Next day the bear is fishing again.
Suddenly he sees a small yellow triangle
coming towards him. At first he is
puzzled.

The triangle becomes larger and larger.
Now the bear sees the dreadful face.
"Help! A monster!" he cries, and runs
away.

"There you are," says Manuel to the
fish. "He's had enough fishing for now."
The fish is happy and says a big thank
you to the mice.

The Bridge

Manuel and Didi are going climbing in
the mountains. In their rucksacks they
have two large apples to take to the
snowman.

As they leave the forest they notice that
someone is following them. It is a
hungry fox.

The fox comes nearer and nearer.
Manuel and Didi walk quickly up the
mountain path to a small bridge. Didi is
afraid.

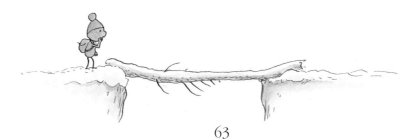

The two little mice run across the bridge
to the other side. The fox is still close
behind them.

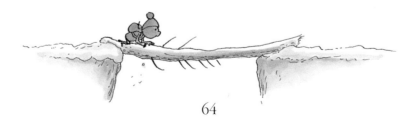

But as the fox tries to step on to the
bridge a lot of snow comes falling down
and sweeps the bridge away.

Manuel and Didi are safe! The fox is
very angry and shakes his fist at them.
But Manuel makes a funny face at the
fox.

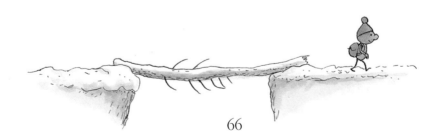

The Snowman

Manuel and Didi climb further up the
mountain. They don't know exactly
where the snowman lives, but with luck
they will find him.

The snowman is always pleased to see
them, and he loves eating their apples.
But now the two mice are in a
snowstorm.

Manuel and Didi find shelter behind a
wall of snow.
"We shall never find the snowman in
this weather," says Manuel.

Suddenly they are startled as the snow
beneath them moves. Then from under
the snow comes the snowman.

"There you are!" cries Manuel. "We have
been looking for you all this time. We
have brought you something nice."
The snowman is very pleased.

He leads them to his warm house.
There they cook the apples on his stove
and tell him all the latest news.

The Badger's House

Manuel has got lost on his walk and is
feeling cold. He rests in a hollow tree. If
the tree had a door he could stay the
night there – but it hasn't.

Manuel leaves the tree and makes his
way through the deep snow. Suddenly
he sees some smoke rising in the
distance. What can it be?

The smoke is coming out of a pipe.
How strange – what is it doing here?
Manuel warms his cold fingers in the
heat.

Then the little mouse has an idea. He
fetches some sticks from the wood and
puts them in the pipe. Now it will get
even warmer, thinks Manuel.

Suddenly a door opens down below
and a badger looks out.
"Are you mad?" he says to Manuel.
"You're blocking up my chimney. Take
those sticks out!"

Then the badger becomes more friendly
and asks Manuel to spend the winter in
his home. Didi is already there, and it is
very cosy for all three of them.

The
Pumpkin Sledge

One day Didi and Manuel see a bird
racing down the mountain on a pair of
skis.

"Terrific!" says Manuel. "I'd love to do
that sometime."

The two mice go along to see the
badger.
"Could you give us one of your
pumpkins?" asks Manuel. The badger is
rather puzzled, but he gives them a
pumpkin.

Manuel and Didi hollow it out. The
badger watches and is even more
puzzled. But Didi guesses what Manuel
is going to do.

Soon they are whizzing down the
mountain on their super pumpkin
sledge. Let's hope it's a good sledge –
there is a lake at the bottom!

Crash! The pumpkin sledge goes
through the thin ice into the water. Hold
tight!

But all turns out well. The pumpkin
floats just like a boat. Manuel and Didi
have a wonderful time.

The Cheese

Manuel and Didi meet a bird who has
stolen a piece of cheese.
"I'm full up now, so you can have the
rest," he says.

He doesn't need to tell them twice.
They eat lots of the cheese. The cold
winter won't be so bad with a full
stomach.

Soon Manuel and Didi are full up. A
large piece of cheese is still left.
"Let's take it to the mountain mice," says
Manuel. "They will be pleased with it."

They carry the heavy cheese up the
mountain. Soon it is evening, but at last
they find the cave where the mountain
mice live.

When Manuel and Didi arrive with their
cheese the mountain mice are all sitting
round an oil lamp trying to keep warm.

The mountain mice are pleased to see
Manuel and Didi and their present of
cheese. It will be a good winter evening
for all of them.